Following tl in Hertfordshi

C000196716

by Michael Stanyon

From the Archives of The Apsley Paper Trail at Frogmore Mill.

Contents

Chapter 1
Paper and Civilisation: 2,000 years of progress

Paper has been integral to the advancement of civilisation for around 2,000 years. Clay tablets and papyrus were early materials. Papyrus had the advantage of being light and flexible, allowing it to be rolled into scrolls. It was made from thin slices of papyrus reed growing in the rivers and marshland around the Mediterranean, providing a durable form of writing material. The name of papyrus gave its name to paper, however, ironically, the definition of paper requires a pulp to have been prepared by mechanical or chemical means, not by weaving as papyrus is.

In Europe parchment or vellum was used by the monasteries to produce exquisitely decorated copies of prayer books and parts of the Bible. The book of the Lindisfarne Gospels, C. AD 700 is well known. Its pages are made of vellum with the 516-page manuscript requiring about 150 calf skins. The Domesday book of 1086 was written on parchment made from sheepskins.

The creation of these documents on such precious materials meant that they were scarce and only for the wealthy. Another material was to emerge from the royal court of China in around 105AD. A legend describes how the eunuch, T'sai Lun, also known as Cai Lun, watched wasps building their nests. He realised that they were chewing wood particles and binding the residues together to make a pale coloured structure.

He reasoned that if he could take plants like mulberry and pound or masticate them into a pulp then he would be able to form the resulting paste into a sheet. Until then the Chinese had used expensive silk cloth to write and paint on.

The knowledge of paper production remained a secret to China, where it was invented, for 700 years. The process gradually moved along The Silk Road trade route which stretched from China to the Western Mediterranean. Silk, unknown in the West, was a principal commodity together with jewellery, perfumes, and ivory, all highly valued by the Mediterranean cultures. In 751AD a battle near Samarkand in modern Uzbekistan is credited with the escape of Muslim slaves: former prisoners, who had the secret Chinese knowledge of making paper.

It would be another three hundred years before the technique reached Spain in 1056. The slow progress into Italy is suggested as having occurred in 1255. The paper museum at Fabriano Mill in Italy, claims that the invention of metal wires forming the mould cover, with additional wires sewn on the surface to form a watermark, had begun there. They also claim that the process of sizing with animal glue to reduce the absorbency was first done there too. At some stage water began to power banks of stampers to beat the pulp, a major improvement from the manual pestle and mortar system of China.

Studies of books and documents in libraries and archives suggests that in Europe a country would be using imported paper for at least a century before they had their own paper mills. Once Europe had caught on to paper's benefits its manufacture began to spread. Reaching Spain in 1056. France in 1338 at Troyes, then Germany in 1390 and finally England in 1488.

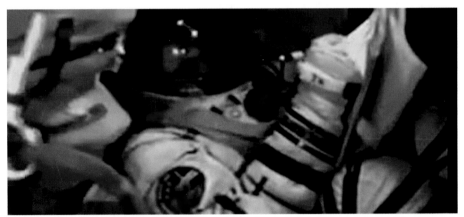

Almost two thousand years after it was invented paper was still needed when Major Tim Peake blasted off to the International Space Station on December 15, 2015. Paper was still a necessity in such a high-tech age.

Chapter 2
Paper Making and Manufacture: an Introduction.

Across Europe the process of papermaking followed a similar pattern. Rags of linen or cotton would be collected, then, at the mill, they would be beaten to a pulp using a water-powered stamper mill before diluting with water. The time for stamping would vary according to the nature of the cloth being treated, often the cloth would first be kept damp to begin rotting before the stamping took place. The process of stamping could take a day or more and so was a factor in the output of the mill. The location of the mill would need to be where there was a stream of sufficient strength all-year round to drive a wheel.

The next stage was to transfer the diluted pulp to a tub, known as a vat. Here the papermaker would immerse a wooden frame with metal wires across it. A second frame without wires, known as a deckle, placed

A German woodcut of 1550 showing the stages of making paper, using waterpower to convert the linen or cotton rags into pulp.

The various stages of beating, pressing, and drying are clearly shown on top would retain some of the pulp as the combined mould and deckle were lifted from the vat. Once removed, surplus water would drain through the wires, aided by a little sideways shake to align the fibres. When the papermaker judged that most of the water had drained from the pulp on the wire, he would remove the deckle. Inverting the mould onto a pad of felt would pull the pulp away from the wire. The mould would now be ready to make the next sheet. The felt would also absorb some of the remaining water. This stage is called couching. Meanwhile another sheet of felt placed on top of the last couched sheet would allow the pile, called a post, comprising alternate layers of pulp and felt, to grow until the whole post could be placed into a press to squeeze out as much water as possible.

As the mould and deckle are lifted out of the vat, water drains through before the deckle is removed.
The wet pulp is now ready for couching the remaining pulp onto piles of felts.

Frogmore Mill's papermaker, Gary Fuller, is seen here couching the pulp onto felt layers to make a post.

Even after the pressing the paper would need to be dried by hanging the sheets in a well-ventilated space, usually a specially built loft with adjustable slats in the walls allowing a through draught. Lofts of this type are extremely rare today although the Apsley Paper Trail's building known as 'The Cottage' at Apsley has vertical slats on its upper storey intended to replicate the look of a drying loft.

When John Dickinson's (now the Apsley Paper Trail cottage at Apsley was given a make-over in the 1920's the upper storey was lined with vertical bars giving the appearance of the louvres of a drying loft.

Before we examine the early paper mills in England, we will first look at how the demand and supply of paper evolved. In the first instance the cost of paper was considerably less than parchment, but demand was most definitely the driving force coming from the increased bureaucracy within government, the legal profession and from large companies like The East India Company. Fortunately, there were plenty of small corn mills around which could easily be converted to provide new sources of paper supply.

Another source of demand came from the printing industry which had expanded in leaps and bounds after Johannes Gutenberg (c. 1400 – 1468), a German goldsmith, invented the first practical method of using moveable, reusable metal type. Before his invention limestone or wooden blocks carrying the required image were used. His invention allowed books to be reproduced faster and in larger quantities than before. The availability of cheaper books marked an improvement in literacy, ushering in a significant stage of progress in human history.

Gutenberg's Bibles each contained 1,286 pages. The number of Bibles he printed is believed to be about 180 with 45 on vellum, each needing the skins of 140 calves! (180 x 45 = 8,100 calves) Demonstrating the need for paper as a cheaper material.

However, hand papermaking remained a slow, laborious process. Some estimates show that a mill could only produce 8 reams a day, or 4,000 sheets using 6 skilled men, plus women and children. One wonders about the vibration of the water powered stamper beaters, imagining that many mills must have been shaken to destruction. How noisy that would have been too, in a world which was otherwise comparatively quiet. In Holland an unrecorded inventor, came up with a solution, later called a 'Hollander' in around 1680, which had many advantages.

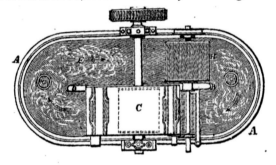

A diagram from an early textbook of 1890 showing top view and section of a Hollander beater.

The pulp circulates in a clockwise direction driven by the blades on the drum which also reduce the material to a pulp.

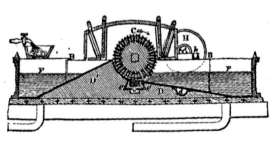

As it was a rotational process the vibration and noise of the earlier stamper beaters was eliminated. Significantly, it was much faster and more productive than the stamper method. Strangely the papermakers were extremely conservative by continuing to refer to beating to the present

6

time. There are several examples of this reluctance to change other terms with technical progress as time went on.

An uninstalled Hollander beater at Frogmore mill waiting to be loaded. The cover over the roll has been removed to show the blades.

This machine formerly worked at Springfield Mill in Kent.

Chapter 3
Hertfordshire and Paper Production:
More than 500 years of history.

Gutenberg's invention in 1450 of moveable type was first introduced to England by William Caxton in 1476 at his press in Westminster Abbey. To begin with all the paper he used was imported, particularly from France.

The London merchant, John Tate set up the first English paper mill on the River Beane, a tributary of the Lea, at Sele mill, Hertford. The date of the conversion is somewhat vague, but it is generally recognized to be around 1488. John Tate was a member of the Mercers Guild and would have travelled on the Continent so had probably seen papermaking there. It is likely that he recruited men from continental mills since nobody in England would have had the knowledge and skills. It is on record that King Henry VII visited Sele Mill in 1498 and 1499 whilst staying at the nearby castle of Hertford. It is also on record that the King gave Tate a small sum of money by way of encouragement.

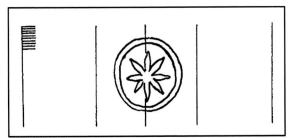

Sele Mill closed soon after the King's visit and there was no other paper mill in the country until the 1550's when a mill was erected at Fen Ditton near Cambridge.

Tate's early watermark, (after Hills).

Sopwell Mill near St Albans was the next Hertfordshire mill to be converted to making paper in 1753 but it burnt down 30 years later. Political problems and taxation made the importation of paper from the Continent very expensive. Changes from stone milling to roller milling being done at the ports using imported grain also made many corn mills redundant so, particularly during the 18th century, many more mills were converted to papermaking. Although many of the 300 or so of the English mills had closed by the middle of the 19th century: they are shown on map which follows. Also note the concentration in the South-east, particularly in Buckinghamshire, Hertfordshire -the Chilterns - and Kent. In these areas the porous chalk holds water which emerges as very pure streams. The more recent extraction of water for human use has massively reduced the amount of water which was once available to drive water wheels.

The improvement of output brought about by the Hollander must have made the drying of the paper a bottleneck in the process, so that required an improvement too. This could only be achieved by building additional drying lofts or developing heating systems to speed the drying.

As previously mentioned, England's first mill was John Tate's Sele Mill in Hertford which only ran between 1488 and 1499. Almost 150 years was to elapse before Sopwell Mill, and later still Hatfield began to make paper. The 18th century brought a rapid increase of 16 more mills although some closed whilst others were opening.

In the 19th century two new purpose-built mills were erected at Home Park and Croxley indicating that something important was happening on the River Gade. Most paper mills had ceased operating by the end of the 19th century concentrating Hertfordshire's papermaking in the Gade Valley.

Several of the closures were caused by bankruptcy but the most bizarre was that of Hamper Mill, near Rickmansworth, which ended abruptly in 1908 when their delivery horse dropped dead.

The table printed below shows the earliest known date of each mill, with the date and reason for the closures. It is very likely that transport problems may have been the reason for the bankruptcies, but also notice that water pollution was beginning to be seen as a problem.

Clearly the River Gade was the emergent centre for mills driven, by excellent transportation and an enterprising and inventive owner. The time would come when the River Gade's mills would become world leaders in output, innovation and diversity of production.

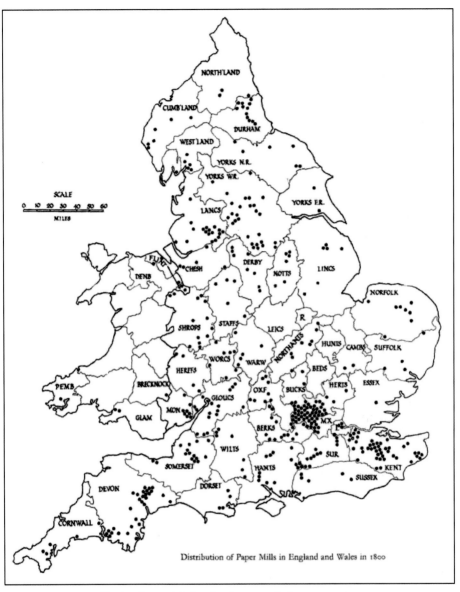

Distribution of Paper Mills in England and Wales in 1800

From *Paper Mills in the British Isles* by Dr A. Shorter, 1971.

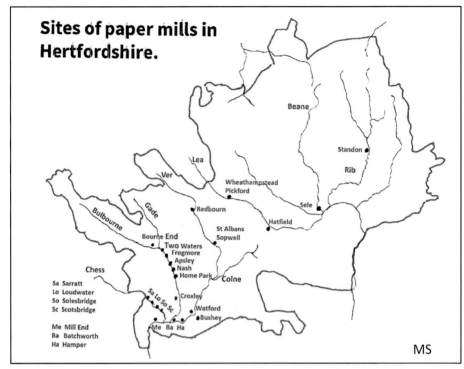

Sites of paper mills in Hertfordshire.

Beane

Standon

Rib

Lea

Ver

Wheathampstead
Pickford

Sele

Bulbourne

Gade

Redbourn

Hatfield

St Albans
Sopwell

Bourne End
Two Waters
Frogmore
Apsley
Nash
Home Park

Colne

Chess

Sa Sarratt
Lo Loudwater
So Solesbridge
Sc Scotsbridge

Sa Lo So Sc

Croxley

Watford
Bushey

Me Mill End
Ba Batchworth
Ha Hamper

Me Ba Ha

MS

This map shows the mill sites printed in red with their rivers in blue. The green indication of Watford is for the location of an engineering works servicing the local industry.

11

Table showing the 21 mill sites in Hertfordshire in the probable order of their opening, together with the date and reason for their closure.

Mill	River	Earliest	Latest	Reason for closure
Sele Mill	Beane	1495	1499	Unknown
Sopwell Mill	Ver	1649	1736	Fire
Hatfield Mill	Lea	1672	1835	Litigation
Standon Mill	Rib	1713	1855	Decline of business
Sarratt Mill	Chess	1742	1871	Decline of business
Redbourn Mill	Ver	1753	1796	Not known
Batchworth Mill	Colne	1755	1887	Transferred to Croxley
Mill End Mill	Colne	1755	1905	Demolished
Scots Bridge Mill	Chess	1755	1885	Pollution
Solesbridge Mill	Chess	1757	1888	Bankruptcy
Loudwater Mill	Chess	1758	1885	Pollution
Two Waters Mill	Bulbourne/Gade	1763	1918	Destroyed by explosion
Bourne End Mill	Bulbourne	1768	1794	Not known
Nash Mill	Gade	1769	2006	Sold for redevelopment
Frogmore Mill	Gade	1774	-	Continuing production
Apsley Mill	Gade	1774	1999	Sold for redevelopment
Pickford Mill	Lea	1775	1849	Bankruptcy
Hamper Mill	Colne	1776	1908	Due to horse dying
Bushey Mill	Colne	1788	1816	Isolated location
Home Park Mill	Gade	1826	1980	Sold for redevelopment
Croxley Mill	Gade	1830	1980	Sold for redevelopment

During the 500 years following Tate's first English mill the demand for paper grew continuously as the essential material for books, newspapers, magazines, diaries, letters, record keeping, packaging and much more. Growth surged from the beginning of the 19th century when paper production became mechanised.

Let us now have a more detailed look at paper making in our corner of West Herts. The Rivers Gade and Chess flowing from the Chilterns provided several mills but the River Wye, in Buckinghamshire, a little further West, supported no less than 31 paper mills on its descent from High Wycombe to the Thames. The Chilterns formed a major papermaking region of England. On the Gade most had been mills from before the time of Domesday in 1086.

Of the mills on the Wye five had been established in the late 17th century and more than half by the middle of the 18th century. It is worth noting that the mills of the Chess were populated between 1742 and 1755, whilst those of the Gade and its tributary the Bulbourne were not populated until between 1768 and 1774. There was a general trend from West to East in the expansion of the industry in the Chilterns. Easy access for transport to London was a definite advantage too.

The need to increase manufacturing capacity had been satisfied by the conversion of older mills to some extent. There had also been some technical improvements like the Hollander Beater described earlier providing a more consistent pulp.

One aspect of papermaking is the skill associated with the manufacture of the moulds themselves, from the drawing of the brass wire to the accurate machining of the wooden rib members. Finally, the attaching of the wires and their stitching with finer wires to complete the mould. This sort of work carried out in conditions of poor lighting must have been very demanding. Many papermakers included a watermark symbol to indicate paper of their manufacture. Then in 1794 Parliament decreed that all paper had to have its year of manufacture included as a watermark. Since tax was to be paid on the paper this resulted in draconian regulations to prevent tax avoidance.

Part of a laid wire hand mould used at Nash Mill in 1806 when it was owned by Griffith Jones.

It was during the 18th century that another trend began to take place. Stationers in the major cities began to own mills themselves giving them exclusive control of a mill's output. They also provided finance for mill improvements.

With few new water mill sites remaining additional demand would need to come from improved efficiency. It would be many years before steam power became viable, as there were no local coal resources. When eventually steam began to become a significant power source it was due to the nearness of a navigable waterway. The arrival of a canal close to the river Gade allowed simple transport of this heavy raw material from the Midland coalfield.

Until then, waterpower remained the only power source because steam was not yet viable in the south of England. The subject of waterpower will be examined later in Chapter 7.

Chapter 4
The Paper Valley: The Gade Valley,
birthplace of paper's industrial revolution.

A limitation of handmade paper is that as each sheet was individually made by a craftsman; the largest sheet possible was limited by how far apart the papermaker could place his arms, about 42inches (107cms). Therefore, large sheets for maps, charts, and wallpaper etc., could only be achieved by pasting sheets together. Innovation was necessary.

Many people tried to develop a method of making paper by a continuous process. The first person to have a practical idea was Nicolas-Louis Robert, a Frenchman. Note that since he was French Nicolas is spelled without an 'h' and we pronounce his name the French way, 'Roberr', with a silent 'T'. Robert lacked the money to develop his idea, although he did obtain a French patent for his scheme in January 1799.

Unable to develop his idea further during the period of the French Revolution he was forced to sell it. Leger Didot, Robert's employer, thought there would be a better opportunity to sell the patent in England. Didot's brother-in-law, John Gamble, was employed travelling between France and England arranging the exchange of military prisoners. Gamble was therefore ideally placed to arrange the transaction. In due course Henry and Sealy Fourdrinier, two brothers from a family of wealthy London Stationers bought a share of the patent. Gamble had copies of the French patent annotated with English measurements to obtain an English patent for the device. (Pat. No. 2487)

The Fourdriniers were businessmen rather than engineers causing them to acquire the services of a skilled engineer to develop the basic idea further. They approached John Hall, a well-known millwright from Dartford in Kent who already did work for them. Whilst he was interested in the project, he recommended one of his former apprentices, Bryan Donkin, who had a mould making business. Since his workshops were not equipped for making machinery the Fourdriniers financed the building of a workshop for him in Bermondsey.

Marchant Warrell, said to be the first machine papermaker.

The Robert prototype machine had been brought over from France allowing for experiments and improvements before it was set to work in Frogmore mill in 1803, where the Fourdriniers were already making paper; they also operated Batchworth and Two Waters mills on the River Gade.

The operation of the machine is believed to have been overseen by Marchant Warrell said to be the first machine papermaker. His family followed in his footsteps in the industry, some going as far afield as Australia and America.

The Gade had the advantage of a road running alongside the river, this being the turnpike road joining London and Aylesbury. At Watford the river was bridged to take the road directly towards London making deliveries along the twenty miles by road very simple. A journey there and back on the same day was quite practical, giving them an advantage over the mills on the Buckinghamshire River Wye which would have been about thirty miles.

In a few years' time transport would become a key factor in the development of the Gade's mills. The recent construction of a canal to London from the Midlands, with a connection nearby from Two Waters to the Thames at Brentford became crucial in the development of this local industry.

Many lessons were being learned from this first attempt to make paper on a commercial scale. Initially the design of the machine itself needed refinement. Whilst Robert had imitated the hand process by including a

16

mechanism to shake the conveyor sideways, he had not understood that couching onto felt helped to lift the wet paper from the wire. Donkin's improvements included adding a felt covered couching roller and press rolls to squeeze out more of the water. In addition, he added a mechanical agitator to prevent the pulp from settling.

The next version of the machine incorporating further improvements in the way that the pulp was delivered to the wire was installed the following year, 1804. This was a somewhat larger machine having increased from 8ft long x 4ft 6ins wide (2.4 x 1.36m) to 27ft long x 4ft wide (8.2 x 1.2m)

A third further improved machine was installed at Two Waters Mill in 1805, this was much larger and capable of making paper 54 ins wide (1.37m).

A replica of Robert's idea displayed at Frogmore mill.

The concept was developed by Bryan Donkin funded by the Fourdriniers to make the world's first practical papermaking machine.

Bryan Donkin was a brilliant engineer making many more machines for the Fourdriniers, but sadly the payments for the machines and royalties were insufficient causing the Fourdriniers to become bankrupt. The consequent inventory of Two Waters Mill in 1810 by Hall and Donkin included large amounts of cast iron, lead and copper piping and a boiler for heating the loft, showing that the faster output from a machine had required improved drying to keep pace with production.

The amount of investment expended by the Fourdrinier brothers has been immortalised today by machines, continuing to use the principle of a conveyor, being known as Fourdrinier machines. Heated cylinders were added to the machine to dry the paper, so the drying loft and all its handling was eliminated. This was a huge improvement but made the machine longer because of the many heated cylinders required. Within a few years the Fourdrinier conveyor design had all the basic elements of a modern machine.

The last two centuries have seen machines become very much larger. The speed of production has increased from those early days when computer control could not have been imagined. A recently opened mill at Kings Lynn, using the Fourdrinier principle, now makes newsprint from recycled newspaper and is one of the world's widest machines at 10.63 metres wide (35ft) producing 400,000 tonnes p.a.

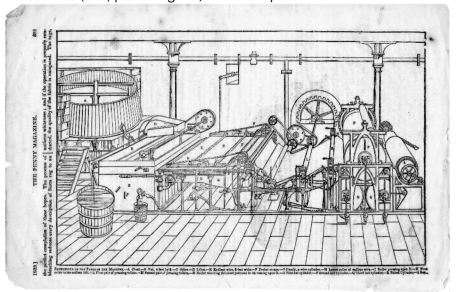

By 1833 the Fourdrinier design had improved. The pulp was now held in a chest, agitated by a paddle, before descending to a flow box to be spread on the wire. More rollers completed the process. From an early edition of The Penny Magazine.

When watching a machine of this type working it is amazing to see the liquid pulp pouring onto the wire, and in a short distance the water being removed sufficiently so that the pulp can support its own weight before going to the couching rolls and beyond. Modern machines also have a suction device below the wire to help draw the water from the pulp.

On Frogmore's Pilot machine this is the magic moment when, after extracting much of the water from the liquid pulp the paper is strong enough to transfer from the wire to a felt sheet for additional pressing and drying.

A view of the 'dry end' of the mothballed No.2 paper machine at Frogmore Mill, which was bought second hand. It first ran there on October 28, 1907
The distant figure gives an indication of its size.

Bryan Donkin

Bryan Donkin (1768 – 1855) was a brilliant engineer who later became the inventor of complex machines for engraving anti-forgery printing plates. His projects included the development of printing processes, astronomical and optical instruments. The breadth of his abilities is demonstrated by his involvement in the first tunnel under the Thames.

In his earlier years he generally improved on the ideas of other people. His outstanding development was the sealable metal can for preserving food which we still use today. It is quite possible that it was his enthusiasm for building new paper machines that led to the bankruptcy of the Fourdrinier brothers.

The majority of Donkin's archive is held at the Derbyshire Record Office where the artistic quality of his machine drawings can be seen. The remarkable clarity of the work demonstrates another aspect of the quality and excellence of his standards.

Chapter 5
John Dickinson: Gade Valley Pioneer, entrepreneur and inventor

John Dickinson F.R.S. (1782 – 1869) a remarkable young man now appears on the scene. Dickinson was not a trained engineer, but as the son of a sea captain based at Woolwich, and having access to the naval workshops there, he must have had a good grounding in practical engineering matters. His career as a stationer began when he was apprenticed to Thomas Harrison on his

fifteenth birthday, during this time he bought paper from George Stafford of Apsley mill and undertook business on his own account.

At the completion of his apprenticeship, he was admitted to the Stationers' Company on 6 March 1804, which was the year after the first machine had been installed at Frogmore. In that same year he filed an affidavit specifying a completely different way to make paper by machine. Instead of the wire conveyor system he used a partly submerged hollow brass cylinder covered with wire gauze to lift the pulp from the vat into the drying stages.

The idea was imperfect and needed improvement. It is believed that this work was done on the roof of Andrew Strahan's office. Strahan was a family friend living with the Dickinson family, who was the King's Printer. Strahan was a considerably wealthy man who would come to lend John Dickinson large sums of money to advance his ideas, having already been instrumental in arranging Dickinson's apprenticeship. Through the naval contacts of his father, Dickinson had heard of the terrible consequences of the muzzle loading cannons firing prematurely. The cause was smouldering residues of the paper cartridges which held measured amounts of gunpowder, continuing to smoulder after firing. Swabbing out with a wet sponge was not always adequate. Frequently, when the next charge was being loaded, a premature explosion occurred causing injury to the gun's crew. Although paper was always made with vegetable fibre Dickinson experimented and found that adding 30% of wool to the mix would make the paper self-extinguishing. So successful was this that the navy considered Dickinson to be the foremost expert on cartridge papers. Dickinson's first patent for cartridge paper was in 1807.

In 1809, at the same time as he patented his improved cartridge paper specification, he also registered the cylinder mould machine. Not only that

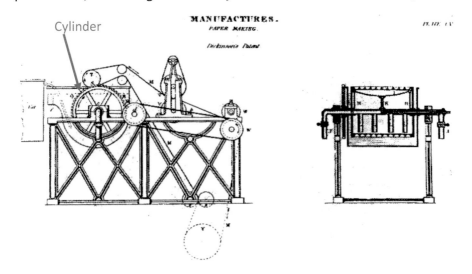

The Cylinder Mould of 1811 showing improvements from Dickinson's earlier scheme. (Patent 3452)

but he managed to raise enough money in loans to buy Apsley Mill, which was conveniently to the north of London; Owen's timetable of 1822 shows that Two Waters, a short walk away, was only 22 miles from Tyburn on the stagecoach route to Aylesbury. A partnership with George Longman MP was needed to finance the purchase. The company of Longman and Dickinson was formed. Then in 1811, Dickinson bought Nash Mill too where he lived for several years. He also married Ann Grover, daughter of a wealthy Hemel Hempstead banker. Yet he was still not thirty years of age!

The rapid increase in paper production brought about by the new mechanised processes had several effects. One was the reduction in the price of paper which immediately increased the demand too. Many of the smaller mills became uneconomic causing many bankruptcies, and finally the supply of rags needed for making paper began to limit production.

Many solutions were explored, one of which was to convert wood into a pulp, this will be explored late in Chapter 6.

A successful solution was to boil esparto grass, found around the Mediterranean deserts, in a caustic solution but for a shorter time than wood required. Since this was the era of steam shipping, when coal from the mines around Newcastle was being taken to the Mediterranean ports, the ships were able to return with a cargo of esparto grass.

A successful mill to do the conversion was created at the Ford Works near Sunderland. It must be assumed that the effluent was discharged into already heavily polluted River Wear there which was close to the sea. The Dickinson directors formed the management Board for this venture which was then able to supply the Dickinson mills with this prepared material.

To complete the esparto conversion begun at Ford Mill, Dickinson's took out a ten-year lease on Two Waters Mill and Frogmore Mill to beat the esparto into half-stuff. Eventually processes were developed to reclaim a large amount of the useful chemicals remaining in the effluent.

Chapter 6
The British Paper Company at Frogmore Mill, a vital link between the mechanisation of paper and today.

The search for alternative fibres to replace the cotton and linen fibres which were desperately needed due to the increased demand for paper began to focus itself on Frogmore Mill. It had long been known that many other vegetable materials, including wood, could be made into a suitable pulp. However, there were obstacles to overcome before this would become practical. The chemical industry was not well developed at the time, and the knowledge of chemical processes was in its infancy. Although it was known that wood could be treated to make pulp it was costly and created copious amounts of effluent which could not be discharged into the rivers, due to the vocal members of the fishing clubs.

However, two men, Hugh Burgess and Charles Watt, were the first to convert sufficient wood into pulp to print part of an edition of the *London Journal* in 1851, using wood pulp paper made at Frogmore Mill. Another 'first' for Frogmore Mill and for the Gade Valley!

There was little interest in this country until improved chemical technology made it possible to treat the effluent produced. Meanwhile, the idea was welcomed in America where rags were scarce and timber plentiful. There the wood was boiled under pressure in caustic soda for up to ten hours. A decidedly risky process.

In 1887 the Potosi Estate Company used Frogmore to make half-stuff from different vegetable fibres including bamboo. Two Waters Mill, a short difference up stream came under joint ownership with Frogmore several times. One such event began after Herbert Sanguinetti, of Italian Jewish extraction, began to make paper barrels at Two Waters. The raw material for this was recycled paper. By 1890 The British Paper Co. had taken Frogmore as its base to make paper products from recycled paper. This company would continue to make paper this way here for over one hundred years. The idea of recycling previously used paper to combat the shortage of raw materials was farsighted, and avoided useful paper being thrown away. At first it was not suited to making good printing paper, although it was excellent for wrapping, packaging and uses like bus and train tickets which were in high demand, but the paper did not command the high prices available for writing and printing papers. Frogmore had yet again forged a new purpose and position in the industry.

The company finally ceased manufacture in 2000 after which the site has been operated by the Apsley Paper Trail as a museum of paper history.

Chapter 7
200 years of John Dickinson & Co.:
A company that helped shape the Gade Valley

When John Dickinson bought Apsley and Nash Mills the Grand Junction Canal joining the Midlands to London had inconveniently been built on the opposite side of the valley to his mills. What was worse, the canal was robbing the river of some of the water needed to turn his waterwheels. In characteristic fashion he set about persuading the canal company to re-route their waterway. When that failed, he went to law proved his case and obtained an Act of Parliament to change the course of the canal. The work was completed in 1818. At the same time, he arranged with the Hertfordshire magistrates to alter Red Lion Lane to its present course, allowing him to create a parkland opposite his house at Nash Mills. In time this would eventually provide room for expansion at Nash Mill.

He must have been very pleased with the result because the canal now ran through land which he owned, providing easy access for his mills to barge transport. Before long he had canal depots near Paddington and later, Kings Cross, to provide deliveries into London. Links to the London Docks for imported rags and esparto grass, and to the Midlands for coal, would allow steam power to develop. His first steam engine at Apsley in 1815 showed that this would become an essential source of power.

Nevertheless, Dickinson had been buying land along the river downstream and ploughing profits into expanding his business. By 1826 he had built a new mill called Home Park at Kings Langley, where Home Park Link Road runs today. Since waterpower was free energy, he built his waterwheel alongside the canal lock to make use of the fall of water there. Hungry to expand he next arranged with Caius College, Cambridge, to use some of their land at Croxley Common. A private Act of Parliament was needed to buy the land. Lord Ebury, who could see the planned mill from his house, insisted that it should be designed with an Egyptian style façade fashionable then. Dickinson had now completed expanding his manufacturing base, although there would be many extensions and additions within those sites in future years.

We have already seen that John Dickinson had Fifteen patents with some of the patents incorporating several concepts. One such idea was to reduce the risk of banking forgeries by introducing coloured threads into the wet pulp, so making the paper unique. In years to come this idea would evolve into the metal strip in our bank notes. When the Post Office decided to restructure the postage system, Dickinson suggested that his silk thread paper should be used for the wrappers sold by the branch offices, so as to foil forgers. Introduced in May 1840, at the start of the Universal Penny Post, these were known as Mulready envelopes after the artist who designed them.

Although the idea was adopted it did not last long before other paper manufacturers objected to Dickinson's monopoly. Then, when postage stamps were introduced, including the penny blacks, they too used the silk thread paper for several years. The upsurge in postal traffic meant that Dickinson began to be a manufacturer of paper products and not just a manufacturer of paper.

Following Dickinson's death in 1869 the company continued to prosper. The growth of a business empire had begun. Apsley ceased to make paper in the late 1880's to concentrate on stationery production, using paper from the other sites. The emphasis on the title of 'mill' was gradually moving towards the concept of 'factory' as a wide variety of paper products were being produced.

The first envelopes, originally called 'pockets', were hand folded; by 1851 machines had been developed when three million were being made every week at the Dickinson sites. Expansion was so rapid that in 1894 individual orders came to be measured in millions; one was for three million 'pence' bags for the Salvation Army. When the Post Office introduced blank postcards in 1870 a major new product family was introduced. Writing paper, compendium boxed sets, and domestic stationery ranging from paper doilies to tablecloths as well as a wide range of printer's requirements. A very large book department made wide a range of leather-bound ledgers.

In 1918 Dickinson's acquired the share capital of a Tottenham based stationer called Millington's. They were a business-like company who had acquired the rights for making window envelopes and had introduced high-speed American rotary envelope machines. The company had recently introduced a new range of stationery which they called Basildon Bond, a high-quality watermarked stationery at a low price. Other domestic products were given the Lion Brand trademark, with printer's stationery, including part printed menus and wedding and party invitations, taking the Aldbury brand name.

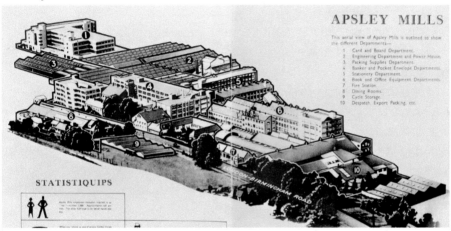

The Apsley mills site in 1937 when 5,000 people were employed there.

By 1937 the Apsley site had expanded to the extent that about 5,000 people were working there. The picture above gives an indication of the scale of the factory. A rail link into the site was refused but in September 1938 a brand-new passenger station was built to serve the factory. An ambitious plan to build a new five story Art Deco style building on the site had to be abandoned due to the worsening conditions prior to the war.

So many envelopes were being made in a vast range of sizes that there were two major departments for administration. These were called Banker, dealing with envelopes having the flaps along the long edge. and Pocket for the envelopes with the flaps on their short edges.

On the outbreak of war in 1939 the company underwent a radical change. Large numbers of men left to join the services with their places taken by women. Munitions work was undertaken with banks of machines, presses, drills, lathes and plastic moulding machines replacing much of the previous manufacture. Paper-based products that were made included containers for explosives and perhaps the most significant was the three thousand tons of strips of laminated paper and metal foil used to drop from aircraft, to trick the enemy radar into believing that an invasion fleet was approaching from a false direction on D-Day.

Other products included petrol pumps, engine magnetos and more than three million sparking plugs. Aircraft engine nacelles and fuel drop tanks to extend the range of fighters were made of laminated and moulded paper at Apsley too.

Prior to the war the company had established many branches in this country and abroad. The financial toll on the nation in the years after the war demanded an export drive to earn foreign currency. By 1954 the company had expanded to 14 UK branches, mainly stockists, and 31 abroad, mainly in what are now Commonwealth countries. At Nash Mill a brand-new machine house was built in the late 1950's.

In the 1960's new premises were built on the Belswains Lane side of the canal allowing the earlier buildings on London road to be demolished to make way for a retail park. Part of the Belswains Lane site was dedicated to produce continuous computer stationery, a reflection of the changing needs of the time. In a changed political and financial climate, it became necessary in 1966 to merge with E.S & A Robinson, a Bristol based company which specialised in packaging and medical uses of paper, later to be known as DRG, the Dickinson Robinson Group. In 1980 a massive new warehouse was erected on the Apsley site where the Holiday Inn now stands. This was an automated storage facility connected to the Belswains Lane site by a new bridge over the canal. Robot tugs transported material around the site and over a new bridge into the warehouse.

As times became more difficult Home Park and Croxley Mills both closed at the end of 1980. Then, in 1987, an aggressive bid by Pembridge Investments Ltd broke up the entire DRG company. In 1990 Biber Holdings acquired the Apsley site with the business eventually to be bought by Spicers before being sold to Hamelin Paper Brands, a French company. Also, in 1990 Sappi Europe (South African Pulp and Paper Industries) bought the Nash Mill site which closed in 2006 to be redeveloped for housing. The original house lived in by John Dickinson remains although considerably altered.

Aerial views of Apsley in 1964 (left) and Nash Mills c.1990 (right) and Croxley in 1948 (below).

Chapter 8
Paper's built legacy in the Gade Valley:
Ever present ways to connect with the past.

The location of each entry is given in OS grid reference and what3words format.

Nash Mill House   **TL 070045**   **salon.active.cove**

Nash Mill is first known to have made paper in 1769. The house is believed to have been built by the mill owner, Griffith Jones. in the late 1700's. John Dickinson bought the mill and lived here from 1811 until he moved to Abbots Hill which we will see later.

After this, Dickinson's partner, Charles Longman lived there until he moved to Shendish House (now called Shendish Manor). In the later years of Nash Mill House, it was a home for Sir John Evans, Dickinson's nephew, and son-in-law, who lived here until 1906 when it became offices. More recently the house was virtually demolished without permission by a developer, but it has been more sympathetically restored as we can see below.

The redeveloped Nash Mill House today still retains much of the original features

Other notable people who lived there include Sir Arthur Evans, Son of Sir John, who was the noted excavator who discovered the Minoan civilisation remains at Knossos, some of which was reconstructed with money from his father. Arthur was also responsible for creating the Ashmolean Museum at Oxford. His brother, Lewis Evans who went on to head up the company, founded the Dickinson Fire Brigade and became Lord Lieutenant of Hertfordshire. Finally, Dame Joan Evans, half-sister of Arthur and Lewis, who became a noted antiquarian and wrote the definitive history of John Dickinson & Co. in 1954.

Shendish Manor   **TL 057043**   **chin.gates.with**

Charles Longman was John Dickinson's partner. When he inherited the family publishing fortune, he built Shendish House on the site of a farm in 1856. In 1936 the Directors of Dickinson's bought the house with 90 acres of parkland for £15,000 to create a sport and recreation centre for its employees. When it opened in 1937 it featured a world class bowls rink, cricket, football and hockey pitches and many indoor facilities. Regular open days for a variety of sports and entertainment for employees and their families were held there. More recently it has become a hotel and golf attraction.

Apsley Mill Cottage and war memorial   TL 062049   chat.lowest.paid

Apsley mill is first known to have made paper in 1778. John Dickinson bought it from George Stafford in 1809. The white boarded building is listed Grade II. During a make-over in the 1930's this building was extended, and an oak-panelled board room added. The white vertical boarding was intended to appear to look like the slats of a drying loft for an early paper mill. By this time the Company had become international in scale particularly active in countries of the, then, British Empire.

The garden includes the company war memorial, dedicated in 1922, listing the names of 360 employees who gave their lives during the two

World Wars. At the time of its dedication, it was situated on the other side of the main road.

From the 1890's Apsley Mill had ceased to make paper but instead made stationery products from paper and board made in the firm's other mills. Many well-known products include Lion Brand, Three Candlesticks and Basildon Bond, named after Basildon Park near Reading and not the better-known Basildon in Essex.

The Basildon Bond clock mounted on the end of the cottage tells the time for passers-by. How fortunate that those two words totalled 12 characters to make the face of this clock.

Apsley Station   TL062048   brings.inform.book

Dickinson's had wanted a rail link for their goods traffic at Apsley to avoid the journey to Boxmoor (now Hemel Hempstead) station or the former Hemel Hempstead station then in Midland Road. In the end they were only able to have a passenger station which was formally opened on 22nd September 1938 when a train broke through a ceremonial sheet of paper.

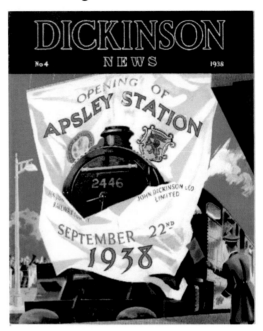

The station remains today as part of an important commuter route.

Holly Bank   TL061050   adults.fixed.monks

An unusual red brick group of four cottages designed by the famous architect Sir Edward Lutyens in 1888. They were built by Arthur Hampton Longman for his estate workers but subsequently bought by John Dickinson & Co.

St Mary's Church   TL 060051   dinner.risks.scam

St. Mary's Church, Grade II listed. Dedicated in 1871, it was built in the Gothic Revival style with much of the finance for the work coming from the Partners of John Dickinson & Co.

As the population of Apsley grew it became necessary to provide many facilities for those living nearby.

Frogmore Mill   TL 058055   line.enhancement.scam

Frogmore mill seen from the bridge on Durrant's Hill. This is an ancient mill and full of history due to the inventions and 'firsts' which have occurred here. It is first known to have made paper in 1774 having previously been a corn mill and a fulling mill. It is now a museum of papermaking.
See www.frogmorepapermill.org.uk

Site of former Two Waters Mill   TL054058   chip.intelligible.sharp

This recently erected apartment block called Riverside is close to the site of the former Two Waters Mill. This was an ancient mill which made paper but was destroyed in an explosion in November 1918.

Nash Mills School   TL 068048   than.chemistry.food

An early Sunday School for village children was first held in the workrooms of Nash Mill. John Dickinson was soon to build this village school in 1847. It has since been considerably extended

Stephenson's Cottage   TL 070046   summer.wants.ritual

Opposite Bunkers Lane is this little cottage which is now a children's nursery. It was built for Leonard Stephenson by John Dickinson who had recruited Stephenson

when he was building the London & Birmingham Railway in around 1837. Stephenson was not related to the famous engineering family although he had trained under Robert Stephenson. He designed and built several steam engines for the mills and established an engineering department at Nash.

Nash Mills War Memorial   TL 070045   hosts.poet.dined

Next to Stephenson's cottage is a grassed garden containing the war memorial bearing the names of former mill workers who had given their lives.

Home Park Cottages   TL078024   behave.cats.names

At Home Park, Kings Langley, these workers cottages were built by John Dickinson in 1825. Typically, they only had one door as Dickinson said that more than one was not needed.

Abbots Hill School   **TL 071045**   **drums.herb.catch**

The house which John Dickinson built for himself in 1836 is at the top of the drive and is now a girl's school. This is the front door at the rear of the

building which was the only door. Dickinson who designed the house thought that more than one was not necessary.

Booksellers Provident Retreat TL081016   poet.tags.latter

When the railway was opened in 1837 it cut through much of the land owned by John Dickinson. One piece near Kings Langley station was donated by him as a home for retired booksellers, with a palatial home being built there. After it had been opened in July 1846 Dickinson was finally accepted by the local gentry.

Timeline/Glossary/Bibliography

Timeline

1488	Sele Mill started by John Tate
1799	Nicolas Louis Robert's French patent
1803	First working Fourdrinier machine installed at Frogmore Mill.
1804	Dickinson's affidavit describing his cylinder mould idea.
1809	Dickinson buys Apsley Mill.
1809	Dickinson patents cylinder mould m/c and cartridge paper.
1811	Dickinson buys Nash Mill.
1826	Dickinson builds Home Park Mill.
1830	Dickinson builds Croxley Mill.
1840	Dickinson uses his silk thread patent for Mulready envelopes.
1846	Dickinson gives land for Booksellers Provident Retreat.
1862	Dickinson Retires.
1869	Dickinson Dies.
1886	John Dickinson and Co. Ltd. Formed from a private company.
1966	Merger with Robinsons of Bristol to become DRG.
1999	Sites of Apsley and Nash Mill sold for redevelopment.

The Gade Valley, is where--

Inventions that changed our world first saw the light of day.

The first Fourdrinier conveyor paper machine and first cylinder mould machines were developed.

Paper was made using a variety of materials including Recycled paper.

Stationery products were developed and made, and many thousands of people employed.

After more than 200 years the Fourdrinier conveyor and cylinder Mould principles remain the mainstays of paper production world-wide.

Recycling is now more important than ever.

Glossary

Beater	A more modern name for a Hollander, used for making machine ready undiluted pulp. It comprises an oval tank with a central dividing spine and having a rotating drum fitted with blades on the circumference which mate with similar blade set in the trough below the drum.
Breaker	A form of Beater or Hollander used for making Half Stuff.
Cartridge Paper	A tough paper used to hold measured amounts of gunpowder to be used in cannons and guns. In 1809 John Dickinson patented a method in which 30% of the pulp was of wool which reduced the risk of the cartridge continuing to smoulder when the next load was being inserted.
Couching	The process of transferring a sheet of handmade paper onto a felt pad prior to compression for squeezing out surplus water.
Cover	A fine woven wire sheet which covered the wires of a mould to produce a smoother surface suitable for high quality printing.
Dandy Roll	A hollow wire cylinder which touches the surface of the wet pulp prior to the couch rolls which can also impart a watermark to the paper when using a Fourdrinier conveyor machine.
Deckle	A wooden frame which fits on the wire side of a mould to prevent the pulp from spilling over the edges of the mould. It will be removed before couching.
Engine	A term used to indicate any kind of mechanical contrivance.
Fourdrinier	The Fourdrinier brothers who financed the development of N L Robert's idea of an endless wire onto which the pulp was poured have given their names to machines of this type.

Half Stuff	Pulp which has been partially broken but not bleached. It may also be compressed to remove water for transportation.
Hollander	The first rotational method for converting rags into pulp. As its name suggests the idea came from Holland around 1680 to replace the less efficient Stamper system.
Maceration	The mechanical breaking down of fibrous material in the presence of a liquid, usually water.
Journeyman	A skilled papermaker who would travel from mill to mill along a prescribed route. He was paid by 'the journey' rather than receiving regular wages.
Machine	In the early days of the Industrial Revolution almost every mechanical device was also known as a machine.
Mould	Handmade paper used a wooden frame called a mould to support the wires on which the paper would be formed.
Paper	A versatile material produced by macerating the stems of plants or by processing wood through chemical or mechanical means.
Papyrus	Slivers of the stem of the papyrus reed which have been woven to form a sheet.
Parchment	The prepared skin of a sheep or goat which can be used for writing, also see Vellum
Shake	The sideways motion given by the papermaker to the mould which helps to align the fibres of the pulp.
Sol	Corruption of the French word salle meaning a room, often used in connection with the well-lit room where women workers check individual sheets for faults.
Stamper	The mechanical beating using hammers, originally manually but later using waterpower to raise the hammers in a trough.
Vellum	A very high-quality prepared skin of a young animal, particularly a calf, lamb or goat.

Watermark	Shaped wires on a mould which compress the pulp slightly to leave a mark which appears to be slightly transparent on the finished paper.
Wire	The metal wire mesh on a mould which became an endless belt on the Fourdrinier conveyor style of paper machine. Nowadays this function is performed by a perforated plastic sheet which is more flexible.

Bibliography

Sources for further reading.

Papermaking in Britain, 1488-1988, by Richard Hills covers the development of paper manufacture in its various forms.

Passing Through, by Fabian Hiscock, or Alan H Faulkner's *The Grand Junction Canal,* are excellent for canal information.

Bryan Donkin, The Very Civil Engineer 1768-1855, by Maureen Greenland and Russ Day illustrate the work of this remarkable engineer.

The Endless Web by Joan Evans describes the John Dickinson Company up to 1954.

Frogmore and the First Fourdrinier by Austin Pilkington is a privately published book describing the British Paper Company's development until 1990.

Paper Matters, available from The Apsley Paper Trail shop gives an excellent coverage of paper development and the industry. The Apsley Paper Trail's excellent Archive holds these and other minor sources.

The British Association of Paper Historians (BAPH) has an informative website, www.BAPH.org.uk.

The Apsley Paper Trail (APT)

APT is a charitable organisation based in Frogmore Mill, Hertfordshire which is known to have produced paper continuously since at least 1774. After The British Paper Company ceased production in 2000 former storehouses have been converted to exhibition space. As an education charity APT has seen many school and group visits and has been regularly used by individual visitors on the regular open days. Frequent canal trips have been a popular feature.

The site has been used by TV and film crews for many years, even a film team from Japan came to visit. The project is assisted by a thriving volunteer group who undertake everything from printing demonstrations, tour guides, and maintenance work. A professional archivist manages the continually expanding collection of historical material, with the assistance of a team of volunteers.

Additionally, APT owns land at Apsley Mill, the next mill downstream from Frogmore where premises are occupied by small businesses to provide an income stream. This includes the former head office of John Dickinson & Co. in its latter years, including the wood panelled former Board Room.

The John Dickinson Company once had its own brass band which was regularly featured on BBC radio. They are now known as The Hemel Hempstead Brass Band and continue to practice regularly on the Apsley site of APT. In the same way the former fire brigades of John Dickinson's and British Paper Company have continued as volunteers to maintain and preserve equipment including a 1938 Denis Ace fire engine.

More information and current events can be found at the Museum's web site www.frogmorepapermill.org.uk